# Mermaid

Steve Barlow and Steve Skidmore
Illustrated by Jack Lawrence

Franklin Watts
First published in Great Britain in 2015 by The Watts Publishing Group


Cover design by Jonathan Hair
The "2Steves" illustration by Paul Davidson
used by kind permission of Orchard Books



PB ISBN 978 1 4451 4088 9
ebook ISBN 978 1 4451 4087 2
Library ebook ISBN 978 1 4451 4089 6

3 5 7 9 10 8 6 4 2

Printed in Great Britain

MIX
Paper from
responsible sources
FSC® C104740

Franklin Watts
An imprint of
Hachette Children's Group
Part of The Watts Publishing Group
Carmelite House
50 Victoria Embankment
London EC4Y 0DZ

An Hachette UK Company
www.hachette.co.uk

www.franklinwatts.co.uk

## How to be a hero

This book is not like others you have read. This is a choose-your-own-destiny book where YOU are the hero of the adventure.

Each section of this book is numbered. At the end of most sections, you will have to make a choice. Each choice will take you to a different section of the book.

If you choose correctly, you will succeed. But be careful. If you make a bad choice, you may have to start the adventure again. If this happens, make sure you learn from your mistake!

Go to the next page to start your adventure. And remember, don't be a zero, be a hero!

You are a mermaid and heir to the throne of the peaceful Merrow people. You live with your father, King Edmar, in Coral City. You have heard that your enemies, the Tritons are preparing to attack. Keto, queen of the Tritons, wants to capture Coral City.

**Go to 1.**

## 1

You ask your father what he thinks the Tritons will do.

"I have sent messages to Queen Keto, but she has not replied. She won't attack though, we are peaceful people," says King Edmar.

At that moment, the palace is rocked by a thunderous explosion. The seaglass windows shatter.

"Look!" Your father points at a pirate ship. It is travelling underwater in a protective air bubble! Its cannons fire again.

"Those pirates are working with the Tritons!" says your father. "Coral City is under attack! I must send a message to Lana, our wise-woman."

"I'll carry the message to her!" you cry. "I can fight with a sword!"

"No," says your father. "Find a safe place to hide until the fighting is over."

If you want to find somewhere to hide, go to 18.

If you decide to find Lana, the wise-woman, go to 9.

If you decide to fight the Tritons, go to 37.

## 2

You find a door to the palace kitchens and sneak inside.

You are spotted by a Merrow officer. "Halt!" he cries. "Who goes there?"

You draw yourself up proudly. "I bear an urgent message for Lady Tethys!"

"A likely story!" scoffs the officer. "Messengers do not hide in kitchens." He calls to a guard.

The guards lead you to the dungeons and push you into a cell.

**Go to 22.**

## 3

The tunnel goes down, deeper into the Lost Caves.

A long, slim shape strikes at you. It is a cave eel! More eel heads peep out of holes in the tunnel wall. Several lunge at you. You dodge – the fangs of these creatures contain deadly venom!

The eels have no eyes. You wonder how they know where you are.

**If you want to attack the eels with your seaglass dagger, go to 41.**

**If you decide to swim past quietly, go to 27.**

## 4

You head towards the orcas.

The killer whales lash their tails in anger. A lone Merrow is no threat to them – but orcas and merlions are natural enemies!

The orcas charge. You swim between them, unharmed. The merlions scatter, roaring with anger as the orcas drive them off. The orcas have saved you!

**Go to 29.**

## 5

You swim to the sea trench. It is blocked.

You order the guards to let you out. They look unhappy, but obey.

The moment you leave the city, a net drops over your head. Triton warriors move in, weapons raised. You were a fool to choose such an obvious route out of the city!

You sound the conch shell that Lana gave you.

**Go to 48.**

## 6

As the boat passes your hiding place, you sneak out. But the pirates spot you and turn their boat towards you.

A pirate fires a cannon and a iron ball whizzes over your head. It crashes into a rockface and the tumbling stones block your way.

The grinning pirates drag you onto their boat.

"Why are you helping the Tritons?" you cough as you struggle for breath.

"They give us these air bubbles so we can go underwater and hide from the King's ships."

**To try to attack the pirates, go to 10.**

**If you decide to try to trick them, go to 43.**

## 7

You turn tail and swim away in blind panic.

A sickly glow spreads across the cave walls. Vampire squid pour out from the tunnel through which you have just come. Cave eels join them!

There is no way out. You are trapped, at the mercy of the Dweller of the Deep. You must try to reason with the terrible creature.

**Go to 35.**

## 8

"What is Queen Keto doing here?" you demand. "Tethys, you are in league with the Tritons!"

Tethys rises to her feet, her face red with fury. "How dare you accuse me?" She points at you. "To the dungeons!"

The lobster guards lead you away, and lock you in the deepest dungeon in the palace.

**Go to 22.**

## 9

You head for Lana's grotto and tell her about the pirates.

Lana gives a sigh. "Only Tethys, Lady of the Sea, is powerful enough to defeat the Tritons."

"I'll go to Tethys for help!" you cry.

Lana hands you a conch shell. "This is the sacred conch of the Merrows. Blow on it if you are in deadly danger, and it will bring you back here to this time. And now I can tell you how to leave the city safely..."

**If you want to listen to Lana's advice, go to 44.**

**If you decide you have no time to lose, go to 23.**

## 10

You hurl yourself at the startled pirates, attacking them with your seaglass dagger.

But there are too many pirates and they are too strong. What's more, you find it hard to breathe inside the ship's bubble. Soon they grab hold of you.

You realise you cannot fight the pirates. Your only hope is to trick them.

**Go to 43.**

## 11

You leave the shelter of the cliff and swim quickly through the water. Hearing cries from behind, you look back to see a group of Selkies riding swordfish.

Selkies are undersea outlaws. Their leader points at you. "Catch that mermaid – the Tritons will reward us!"

You see a giant seaweed forest ahead.

**To hide in the seaweed forest, go to 17.**

**If you decide to try to outrun the Selkies, go to 39.**

## 12

The moment you are outside the air bubble, you lash your tail and speed away.

The pirates grab their oars. "Don't let it escape!" cries their leader.

Suddenly, a wooden wall lined with cannons rises up in front of you. Another pirate ship! The grinning pirates fire the cannons.

Cannonballs rip through the water towards you. You know there is only one way to escape. You blow hard on your magic conch shell.

**Go to 48.**

## 13

You head towards the glow.

It seems to come towards you. Suddenly, you are surrounded by the bright shapes. Tentacles spread out around their cruel beaks. You recoil in horror. Vampire squid! These dreadful creatures will suck every drop of blood from your body!

There is no escape! As the squid draw closer, you raise the conch shell to your lips and blow.

**Go to 48.**

## 14

As you swim through the city, dodging soldiers and falling buildings, you spot a gap between two attacking pirate ships and slip through.

However, the Triton guards are watchful.

Soon they have you cornered. There is no escape. You raise the conch shell to your lips and blow.

**Go to 48.**

## 15

The right-hand tunnel goes upwards. It is very dark.

You spy movement. The rock of the tunnel wall seems to be moving.

You feel a sting on your arm. You look down to see a bloated white tentacle lying across it. You tear your arm away.

You gasp in horror as you realise that the whole tunnel is lined with the tentacles of a huge hydra anemone.

**If you want to go on, and try to swim through the hydra, go to 32.**

**If you would rather go back and try the other tunnel, go to 3.**

## 16

"Queen Keto is a liar!" you cry.

Tethys is furious. "I will not have guests insulted in my court!" She points at you. "Take the Merrow to the dungeons!"

Finfolk guards, spears at the ready, escort you from the throne room and throw you into a dungeon.

**Go to 22.**

## 17

You reach the forest and move slowly and quietly through the seaweed. Your enemies will never find you in here.

But then you see movement among the seaweed, all around you. What is causing it?

A pair of eyes appear, then two more, each with a tawny muzzle and a dark mane.

You are being stalked by a pride of merlions!

**If you want to stay in hiding, go to 42.**

**If you want to try to get away from the merlions, go to 28.**

## 18

You want to join the fight to save Coral City from the Tritons, but you know you must obey your father.

However, as you swim towards your apartment in a tower of the palace, the pirates' cannons roar again. A shot crashes into the tower, and it crashes down.

You cannot obey your father. There is no safe place to hide. Coral City is doomed unless the wise-woman Lana can help.

**Go to 9.**

## 19

You race towards the palace.

The pirates spot you and chase you. Two boats come up behind you with a net spread between them. Before you can dodge, you are trapped!

The laughing pirates drag you aboard their boat and free you from the net.

"Why are you helping the Tritons?" you cough as you struggle for breath.

"They give us these air bubbles so we can go underwater and hide from the King's ships."

**If you want to try to attack the pirates, go to 10.**

**If you decide to try to trick them, go to 43.**

## 20

"You attacked my city and killed my people," you tell Keto. "You deserve to die!" You prepare to deliver the final blow.

"Halt!" cries Tethys. "You come to me for aid, yet you show no mercy to your enemy. I will do nothing to help such a cruel race."

Your anger has betrayed you. You are led from the palace, and told never to return. Though you are free, you have failed the final test.

You blow the conch shell.

**Go to 48.**

## 21

You launch yourself at the Dweller, striking out with your dagger.

But the seaglass blade cannot penetrate the thick, slimy hide of the hagfish. The Dweller draws you towards its horrible, bristly mouth.

You raise the conch shell to your lips and blow.

**Go to 48.**

## 22

There is no escape from your prison. The walls and door are solid stone.

You know that by the time Lady Tethys releases you – if ever – it will be too late to save Coral City.

You raise the conch shell and blow.

**Go to 48.**

## 23

"Sorry," you say, "there's no time to lose."

You race away from Lana's grotto.

You have to decide on the safest way to leave the city. The Lost Caves will lead you out of the city, but they're very scary. The sea trench would be quickest, but may be watched. Perhaps there's another way?

**If you think you should try the Lost Caves, go to 31.**

**If you would prefer to try the sea trench, go to 5.**

**If you think you should try to find another way, go to 14.**

## 24

You beckon, and swim away. The greedy pirates follow.

When all the pirates are away from their ship, you suddenly swim back round under it, find the plug used to drain the ship when it's out of the water, and pull.

Water rushes into the boat. The air bubble bursts. The terrified pirates swim up to the surface for their lives!

You look around quickly. The other

pirate ship, seeing the men in trouble, is coming up fast. A giant turtle is swimming peacefully overhead. Behind you, a cave seems to offer a perfect hiding place from the pirates.

**If you decide to hide in the cave, go to 40.**

**If you want to swim towards the turtle, go to 30.**

## 25

Your message to Tethys is urgent — but if you are captured, it will never reach her.

You swim in the shadow of the cliff until you come to a coral reef. When you reach the end of the reef, you see two possible hiding places: a wrecked ship and a giant seaweed forest.

**To hide in the seaweed forest, go to 17.**

**If you decide to hide in the wreck, go to 46.**

## 26

You deliver your father's plea for help.

Tethys seems unmoved. "Why should I meddle in the affairs of Tritons and Merrows?"

Queen Keto smirks.

"But the Tritons have done more than attack my people." You tell Tethys about the pirates.

The Lady of the Sea is furious. "Humans cause enough trouble to the people of the

sea even when they stay above its surface," she cries. "I will not have them coming into my realm to create more!" She points at Keto. "Arrest her," she tells her guards, "and see that her army is scattered! The war is over!"

**Go to 50.**

## 27

You swim forwards slowly to not disturb the water. The cave eels cannot tell where you are! Past the cave eels the tunnel divides again. Down one passage, you can see a distant glow. The other tunnel looks dark and forbidding.

**To swim towards the glow, go to 13.**

**If you decide to take the dark tunnel, go to 45.**

## 28

You shoot upwards, leaving the waving seaweed behind. The merlions follow you.

You soon realise that the creatures are

too fast. You cannot outrun them.

Ahead of you, you see a pod of orcas.

**If you want to avoid the orcas, go to 33.**

**If you decide to swim towards them, go to 4.**

## 29

Now, far in the distance, you can see the lights of Tethys's palace.

You begin to swim straight towards the palace; but a giant shadow looms overhead. You look up to see the pirate ship encased in an air bubble!

**If you want to hide from the pirates, go to 38.**

**If you want to trust your speed to get you to the palace, go to 19.**

## 30

You swim up over the turtle and drop down onto its back.

Hidden by the turtle's shell, you pass over the pirate ship.

When the pirates are far behind, you head for Tethys's palace. It is surrounded by a Merrow and Finfolk army.

**If you want to enter the palace by the main gate, go to 34.**

**If you want to search for a back way into the palace, go to 2.**

## 31

You swim from Lana's grotto. Deep beneath Coral City you find the entrance to the Lost Caves. These are so dangerous that no-one has ventured into them for years.

You gaze at the cave-mouth and loosen your seaglass dagger in its sheath. Cautiously, you swim forwards. It is dark in the tunnel, and before long the passage in front of you divides.

**To take the left-hand passage, go to 3.**
**To take the right-hand passage, go to 15.**

## 32

You swim forwards as quickly as you can, hoping that if you move fast enough, the hydra will not be able to catch you.

But soon you are hopelessly caught in the creature's tentacles.You manage to pull an arm free and raise the conch shell to your lips and blow.

**Go to 48.**

## 33

Orcas can be dangerous. You turn away from them, and the merlions do the same. They herd you back towards the kelp forest.

**Go to 42.**

## 34

You swim boldly to the nearest army officer. "I have a message for Lady Tethys!"

The officer beckons you to follow him to the palace.

Guards escort you to the throne room. Tethys, the Lady of the Sea, sits on her great oystershell throne – but you are dismayed to see standing before her Queen Keto of the Tritons, your father's deadly enemy!

**If you wish to accuse Tethys of being in league with your enemies, go to 8.**

**If you wish to greet Tethys with respect, go to 47.**

## 35

"Show yourself," you cry, "and tell me what you want!"

Vampire squid emerge from the shadows. Their glowing bodies reveal the hideous shape. The Dweller of the Deep is a monstrous hagfish!

The Dweller looms over you and the white bones on the cave floor. The foul creature hisses. "Few enter my Lost Caves. No one leaves."

You prepare to fight for your life!

**If you wish to attack the Dweller with your seaglass dagger, go to 21.**

**If you want to look for a more deadly weapon, go to 49.**

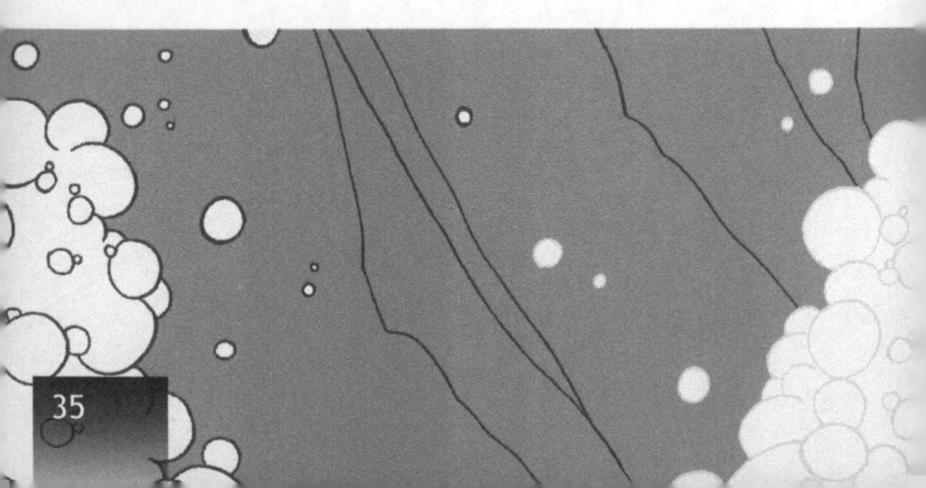

## 36

"I challenge Keto to a duel," you cry. "I will prove that I am worthy to speak for my father!"

Keto raises her sword and lunges at you. You unsheath your seaglass dagger and deflect the blow.

One of Tethys's Finfolk guards throws you a sword. It is your turn to attack.

Queen Keto is strong, but you are quicker. With a lightning strike, you knock the sword from her hands.

Keto spreads her arms wide. "You have beaten me."

**If you wish to strike Keto, go to 20.**

**If you want to deliver your father's message, go to 26.**

## 37

You decide to ignore your father, and join the fight to save Coral City. You find the Captain of the Palace Guard and demand a weapon.

"You know I can fight!" you tell him.

He shakes his head. "No! If anything happens to your father, you will be ruler of the Merrow."

You realise the Captain is right – but if you can't fight, you can at least take your father's message to Lana.

**Go to 9.**

## 38

You hide inside the shell of a giant clam.

As the pirate ship comes closer, you can hear pirates talking.

"Don't see why we have to hunt mermaids for the Tritons," grumbles an oarsman.

The steersman scowls. "The Tritons give us air bubbles so we can hide underwater.

Anyway, who cares what happens to a bunch of fish-tailed flibbertigibbets. I'm only here to find out if the Merrow have any treasure. Keep rowing!"

**If you want to attack the pirates in their air bubble, go to 10.**

**If you want to try to sneak past them, go to 6.**

## 39

You swim away from the Selkies as fast as you can. But their swordfish mounts are too fast. Soon, you are surrounded by deadly blades.

There is no escape. You raise the conch shell to your lips and blow.

**Go to 48.**

## 40

You head for the cave – but as you reach it, a boat rows out! More pirates were lying in wait for you!

The crew are holding wicked-looking

tridents. They are almost in striking distance: there is no escape!

You blow your conch shell.

**Go to 48.**

## 41

You draw your seaglass dagger and attack the nearest cave eel. But the movement attracts more eels. They dart towards you, and strike!

You feel the sting of their venom. With the last of your strength, you blow your conch shell.

**Go to 48.**

## 42

The merlions slowly surround you. You can see the hunger in their eyes. They close in. There is no escape.

You raise the conch shell to your lips and blow.

**Go to 48.**

## 43

"Let me go," you tell the pirates, "and I'll show you some sunken treasure. There's enough gold to make you rich for life."

The pirates' eyes glint greedily. "All right, young Merrow." They untie you. "Take us to the treasure!"

**If you want to try to escape from the pirates, go to 12.**

**If you want to lead the pirates away from their ship, go to 24.**

## 44

"You must leave the city through the Lost Caves," says Lana. "All other exits will be watched. But beware the Dweller of the Deep, who rules the caves."

You thank Lana for her advice, but you are not sure you want to follow it: you are afraid of the darkness and danger of the Lost Caves. Should you try another way?

**If you wish to follow Lana's advice, go to 31.**

If you would prefer to try the sea trench, go to 5.

If you think you should try to find another way, go to 14.

## 45

It is pitch-black in this tunnel. You can see nothing.

Something brushes against your face. You flinch. More stems of seaweed cling to you like clammy fingers.

You break free of the seaweed, and swim out of the tunnel into a large cave.

Something clatters as your tail brushes the cave floor. You reach down, and feel something hard and curved. The floor is covered with bones!

A voice echoes from the darkness. "Welcome to the realm of the Dweller of the Deep."

**If you want to swim away, go to 7.**

**If you decide you must talk to the Dweller, go to 35.**

## 46

You hide in the wreck. Moments later, you hear voices. It's a Triton patrol! Its dogfish find you and start barking.

"Come out!" orders the patrol leader. You do not move.

The Tritons begin to strike the hull. The wreck shakes and timbers fall, pinning you to the seabed.

You manage to drag the conch shell to your lips, and blow.

**Go to 48.**

## 47

You bow low before Tethys. "My father, King Edmar, greets the Lady of the Sea."

Tethys eyes you coldly. "What do you want?"

"The King asks you to stop Queen Keto's attack on Coral City."

"The Merrows attacked my people first!" cries the Triton Queen. "This little Merrow is only a messenger, and has no right to accuse me!"

**If you want to accuse Queen Keto of lying, go to 16.**

**To challenge Keto to a duel, go to 36.**

## 48

A whirlpool forms around you, whisking you away from danger.

The rushing water slows. The whirlpool disappears. You are back in the grotto of Lana the wise-woman.

She shakes her head on seeing you. "Perhaps you are not ready for this task."

"I am!" you tell her. "I must get to Tethys! I am ready to try again."

**Go to 31.**

## 49

Feeling among the bones on the cave floor, your fingers grasp a tusk of a narwhal. You lift it and brace the end against a rock.

You are only just in time. The hagfish charges, and falls onto the tusk.

Quickly you swim past and out of the Lost Caves. You are outside Coral City! You wait in the shadow of a sea cliff. Ahead of you there are enemy patrols, searching the dark waters.

**If you want to head to Tethys's palace as quickly as possible, go to 11.**

**If you decide to try to sneak past the enemy, go to 25.**

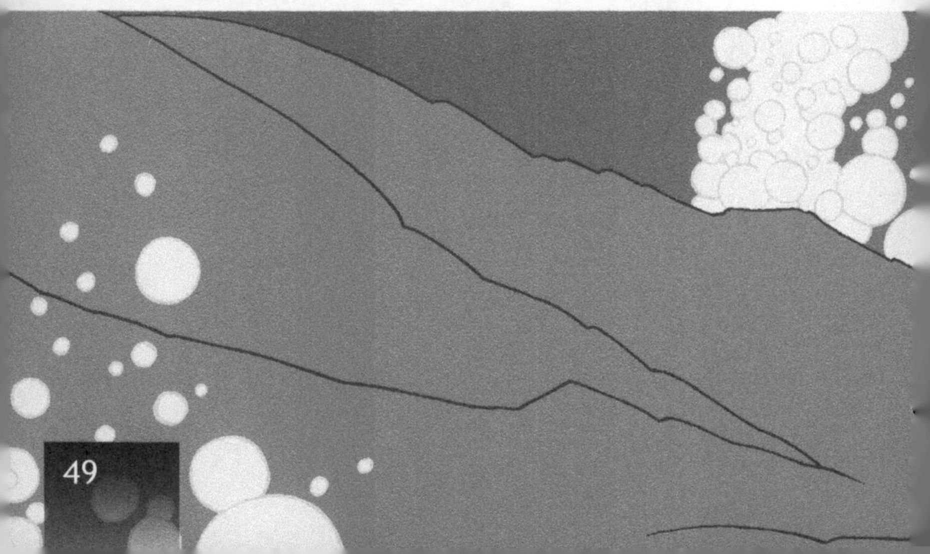

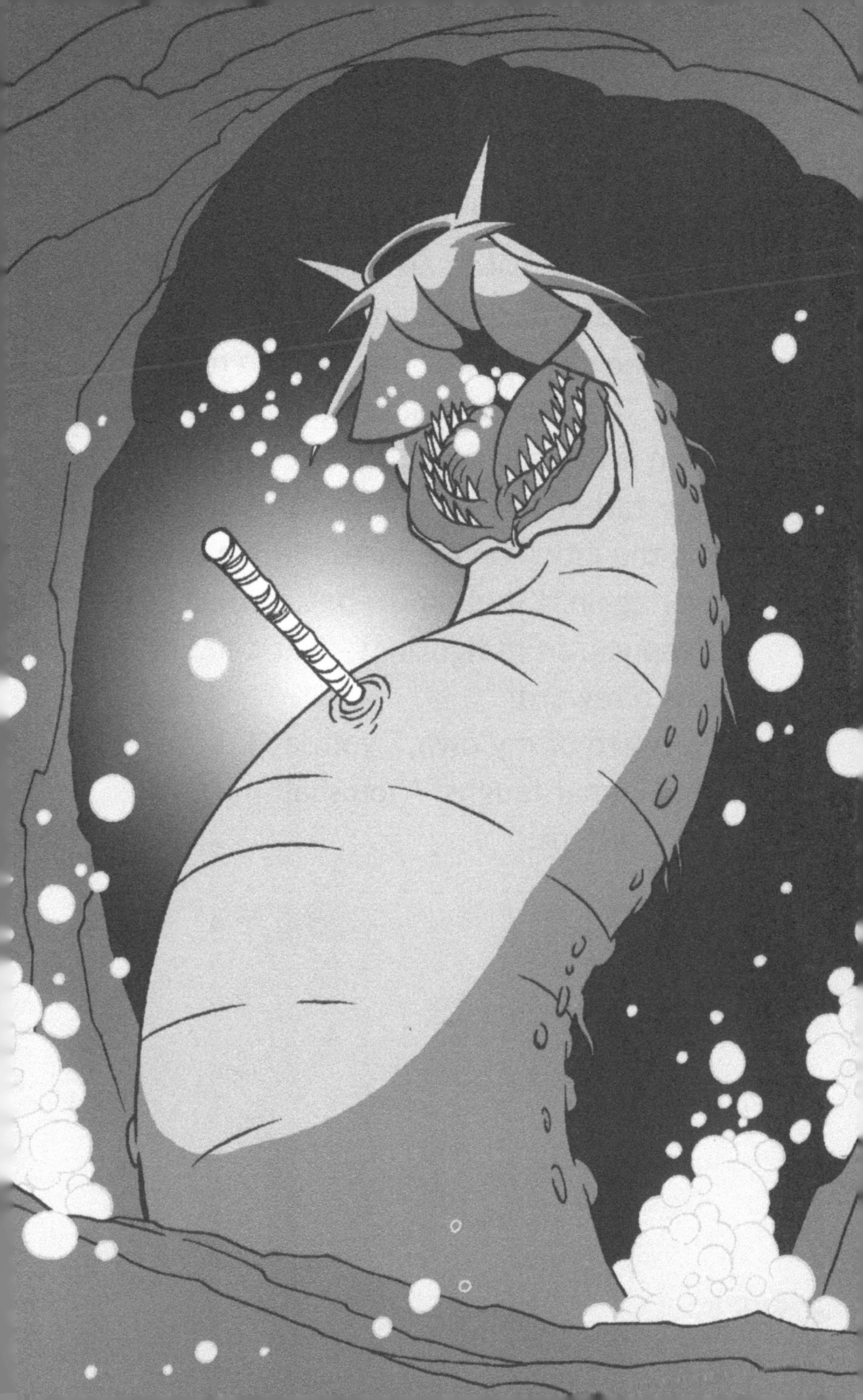

## 50

You return to Coral City to a hero's welcome. The Triton army, along with the pirates, have fled. Tethys's Finfolk soldiers patrol the city to see that they do not return. The damage caused by the pirates' cannon is already being repaired.

Your father takes your hand. "You have saved the city," he declares. "If we ever go to war again, I shall know better than to try to keep you from fighting! What can I offer you as a reward?"

"A sword of my own," you say.

King Edmar laughs. "You shall have it! You are a hero!"

Immortals

HERO

# I HERO Quiz

Test yourself with this special quiz. It has been designed to see how much you remember about the book you've just read. Can you get all five answers right?

To download the answer sheets simply visit:

*www.hachettechildrens.co.uk*

Enter the "Teacher Zone" and search "Immortals".

## Question 1

Who is the only one powerful enough to defeat the Tritons?

A Queen Keto

B Tethys, Lady of the Sea

C Lana, the wise-woman

D The Dweller of the Deep

## Question 2

What is the name of the Merrow home city?

A Crab City

B Coral City

C Cabbage City

D Clam City

## Question 3

Which weapon do you use to defeat the Dweller of the Deep?

A a seaglass dagger

B a sword

C a conch shell

D a narwhal tusk

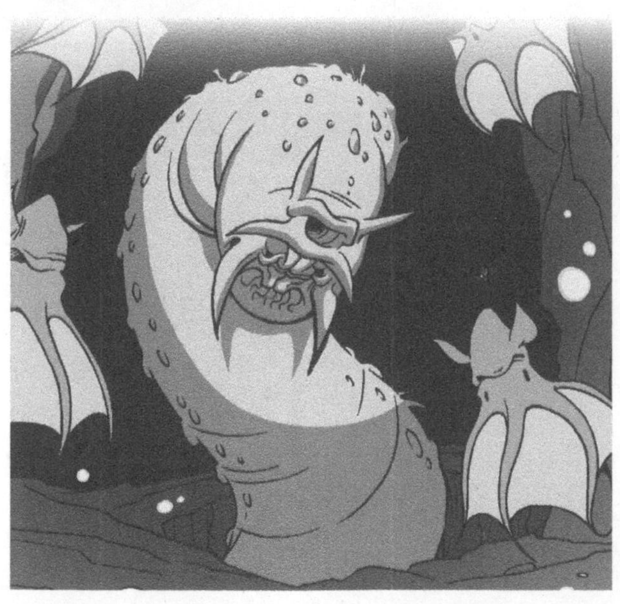

## Question 4

Which magical object does Lana give you?

A a snail shell

B a clam shell

C a conch shell

D a seaglass shell

## Question 5

Who do you duel with in Tethys's palace?

A Queen Keto

B Lana

C King Edmar

D The Dweller of the Deep

## About the 2Steves

"The 2Steves" are Britain's most popular writing double act for young people, specialising in comedy and adventure. They perform regularly in schools and libraries, and at festivals, taking the power of words and story to audiences of all ages.

Together they have written many books, including the *Crime Team* series. Find out what they've been up to at: **www.the2steves.net**

## About the illustrator: Jack Lawrence

Jack Lawrence is a successful freelance comics illustrator, working on titles such as *A.T.O.M.*, Cartoon Network, *Doctor Who Adventures*, *2000 AD*, *Gogos Mega Metropolis* and *Spider-Man Tower of Power*. He also works as a freelance toy designer.

Jack lives in Maidstone in Kent with his partner and two cats.

# Have you completed the I HERO Quests?

## Battle with aliens in Tyranno Quest:

978 1 4451 0875 9 pb
978 1 4451 1345 6 ebook

978 1 4451 0876 6 pb
978 1 4451 1346 3 ebook

978 1 4451 0877 3 pb
978 1 4451 1347 0 ebook

978 1 4451 0878 0 pb
978 1 4451 1348 7 ebook

## Defeat the Red Queen in Blood Crown Quest:

978 1 4451 1499 6 pb
978 1 4451 1503 0 ebook

978 1 4451 1500 9 pb
978 1 4451 1504 7 ebook

978 1 4451 1501 6 pb
978 1 4451 1505 4 ebook

978 1 4451 1502 3 pb
978 1 4451 1506 1 ebook

## Save planet Earth in Atlantis Quest:

978 1 4451 2867 2 pb
978 1 4451 2868 9 ebook

978 1 4451 2870 2 pb
978 1 4451 2871 9 ebook

978 1 4451 2876 4 pb
978 1 4451 2877 1 ebook

978 1 4451 2873 3 pb
978 1 4451 2874 0 ebook

# Also by the 2Steves...

978 0 7496 9283 4 pb
978 1 4451 0843 8 eBook


**A millionaire is found at his luxury island home – dead! But no one can work out how he died. You must get to Skull Island and solve the mystery before his killer escapes.**

978 0 7496 9284 1 pb
978 1 4451 0844 5 eBook


**The daughter of a Hong Kong businessman has been kidnapped. You must find her, but who took her and why? You must crack the case, before it's too late!**

978 0 7496 9286 5 pb
978 1 4451 0845 2 eBook


**You must solve the clues to stop a terrorist attack in London. But who is planning the attack, and when will it take place? It's a race against time!**

978 0 7496 9285 8 pb
978 1 4451 0846 9 eBook


**An armoured convoy has been attacked in Moscow and hundreds of gold bars stolen. But who was behind the raid, and where is the gold? Get the clues – get the gold.**